I0616810

1

Contents

OVERVIEW

Nutrition is a vitally important part of treatment for patients with pancreatitis. The primary goals of nutritional management for chronic pancreatitis are:

- Prevent malnutrition and nutritional deficiencies
- Maintain normal blood sugar levels (avoid both hypoglycemia and hyperglycemia)
- Prevent or optimally manage diabetes, kidney problems, and other conditions associated with chronic pancreatitis
- Avoid causing an acute episode of pancreatitis

To best achieve those goals, it is important for pancreatitis patients to eat high protein, nutrient-dense diets that include fruits, vegetables, whole grains, low fat dairy, and other lean protein sources. Abstinence from alcohol and greasy or fried foods is important in helping to prevent malnutrition and pain.

PANCREATITIS DIET RECIPES

BREAKFAST

1. Kefir Pancakes

Prep: 10 min.

Cook: 10 min.

Total: 20 min.

Yield: 3 Servings

Ingredients

- 1 cup all-purpose flour
- 1 cup oat flour
- 1½ tsp baking soda
- ½ tsp table salt
- 2 cup low-fat Kefir, plain
- 1 cup skim milk
- 1 tsp vanilla extract
- 1 whole egg
- 2 large egg whites
- 3 tablespoon peanut butter, smooth, reduced fat
- 1 cup blueberries

Directions

1. In a large bowl, mix flour, oat flour, baking soda and salt. In another bowl, combine together the kefir, milk, vanilla extract and eggs; beat until well-blended. Next, add the dry mixture to the wet mixture until a moist batter has formed.

2. Pre-heat a skillet on medium heat and spray with non-stick cooking spray. Drop the batter onto the skillet by large tablespoon and cook for 1-2 minutes before flipping and cooking for another minute or two on the second side. Continue until all pancakes are completed.

3. Place the natural peanut butter in the microwave for 20-30 seconds to soften and then drizzle over pancakes; top pancakes with the fresh berries.

2. Blueberry Pancakes

Prep: 10 min.
Cook: 10 min.
Total: 20 min.
Yield: 1 Serving

Ingredients

- 6 large egg whites
- ½ cup raw oats
- 1 tsp baking powder
- ½ cup unsweetened almond milk
- 1 dash table salt
- 2 tsp granulated Stevia
- ¼ cup blueberries
- ½ cup unsweetened applesauce
- 1 dash cinnamon

Directions

1. Put egg whites, oats, baking powder, almond milk, salt, and Stevia in the blender.
2. Blend for 30 seconds on med-high speed.
3. Spray a pan with non-stick cooking spray, pour batter on pan, and add half the blueberries.

4. Cook like a regular pancake.

5. For topping, add applesauce and cinnamon.

3. Basic Protein Pancakes

Prep: 10 min.

Cook: 10 min.

Total: 20 min.

Yield: 1 Serving

Ingredients

- ¼ cup raw oats
- ¼ cup fat-free cottage cheese
- ½ scoop(s) banana or vanilla protein powder
- ½ cup egg whites

Directions

1. Blend all the ingredients until a batter forms. Pour over a hot griddle.
2. Flip when the edges start browning.
3. Serve with a tablespoon of natural peanut butter and top with almonds.

4. Lean Blueberry Pancakes

Prep: 10 min.

Cook: 10 min.

Total: 20 min.

Yield: 1 Serving

Ingredients

- ½ cup egg whites
- ½ small (6" to 6-7/8" long) banana
- 1 scoop Lean Pro 8 protein
- ½ cup oatmeal, cooked
- ½ cup blueberries
- 2 tsp baking powder

Directions

1. Mash the banana and crack the eggs in it, stirring until the mixture becomes somewhat homogenized.
2. Heat a greased griddle or frying pan on medium heat and pour about a 2.5-inch wide puddle of batter.
3. Delicately flip the pancake after about 25 seconds or when it browns. The recipe makes 3-4 small pancakes.

5. Beet Pancakes

Prep: 10 min.
Cook: 15 min.
Total: 25 min.
Yield: 1 Serving

Ingredients

- ½ cup beets, cut into cubes
- ¼ cup oat bran
- ½ tsp baking soda
- 3 egg whites
- 1 scoop(s) vanilla whey protein powder

Directions

1. Place all the ingredients into a blender and puree until well mixed.
2. Pour the mixture onto a greased griddle or pan over medium heat until bubbles form on the surface, then turn over and cook until dark golden brown.
3. Serve with sugar-free syrup.

6. Ground Turkey and Sweet Potato Hash

Prep: 5 min.

Cook: 15 min.

Total: 20 min.

Yield: 1 Serving

Ingredients

- oz 93% lean ground turkey
- 1 sweet potato, cut into cubes
- ½ medium (approx 2-3/4" long, 2-1/2" dia) green bell pepper
- ¼ onion, chopped
- 1 clove garlic, minced
- 1 pinch table salt
- ¼ tsp garlic powder
- ¼ tsp red pepper

Directions

1. Poke holes in sweet potato with a fork. Microwave for 5 minutes.
2. Dice bell pepper, onion, and garlic. Store remainder in fridge for a future meal.

3. Cook ground turkey in a separate skillet. This dish works if you already have turkey cooked ahead of time too.
4. Using a nonstick frying pan, begin to sauté vegetables on medium-high heat.
5. Add salt, garlic powder, and red pepper to taste.
6. Once sweet potato is finished cooking, allow to cool for 2 minutes before handling.
7. Upon cooling, dice sweet potato into small cubes. Add to frying pan.
8. Continue to sauté ingredients until vegetables are tender.
9. Incorporate ground turkey and mix until thoroughly heated.
10. Transfer ingredients to plate, top with salsa, and enjoy!

7. PB & Berry Protein Oats

Prep: 125 min.

Cook: 0 min.

Total: 125 min

Yield: 1 Serving

Ingredients

- ½ cup rolled oats
- ½ cup(s) vanilla whey protein powder
- 2 tsp chia seeds
- ¼ tsp cinnamon
- ⅔ cup low-fat milk
- 1 tbsp natural peanut butter
- ¼ cup raspberries
- ¼ tsp vanilla extract

Directions

1. In a wide-mouth half-pint glass jar, layer in oats, protein powder, chia seeds, and cinnamon.
2. Stir in milk and vanilla if using.
3. Top with peanut butter and raspberries.

4. Seal shut and chill for two or more hours or up to three days.

8. Pumpkin Protein Pancakes

Prep: 5 min.

Cook: 5 min.

Total: 10 min.

Yield: 1 Serving

Ingredients

- 1 scoop MuscleTech 100% Whey Advanced protein, French Vanilla Creme
- 2 tbsp pumpkin puree
- 2 tbsp almond flour
- 2 egg whites
- ¼ tbsp baking powder
- 1 tsp extra virgin coconut oil
- ¼ tsp vanilla extract
- ¼ tsp pumpkin pie spice
- to taste granulated Stevia

Direction

1. Blend all ingredients, and cook as you would a traditional pancake!

9. Mini Italian Frittatas

Prep: 5 min.

Cook: 10 min.

Total: 15 min.

Yield: 6 Servings

Ingredients

- 1 cup egg beaters
- ½ cup asparagus
- 4 oz low-sodium turkey bacon
- ½ tbsp parsley, dried

Directions

1. In a sauce pan, saute asparagus and turkey bacon.
2. Stir together with egg beaters and parsley.
3. Pour mixture into a mini muffin pan and bake at 375 for 8-10 minutes.

10. Peanut Butter Banana Waffles

Prep: 10 min.

Cook: 15 min.

Total: 25 min.

Yield: 2 Servings

Ingredients

- ¾ cup whole-wheat flour
- 1 scoop Signature Vanilla Whey Protein Powder
- 1 bar Signature Protein Crunch Bars, Chocolate Peanut Butter
- 1 tbsp PB2 powdered peanut butter
- ½ tsp cinnamon
- ¾ tsp baking powder
- ¼ cup almond milk
- 1 tbsp almond milk
- 1 whole egg
- 1 cup nonfat plain Greek yogurt
- 1 medium (7" to 7-7/8" long) banana, sliced
- ½ tsp vanilla extract

Directions

1. Preheat waffle maker to medium heat.

2. Whisk together flour, protein powder, PB2, cinnamon, and baking powder.

3. In a separate bowl, mash banana until smooth. Add egg, Greek yogurt, almond milk, and vanilla extract, and mix well.

4. Add the wet ingredients to the dry ingredients and gently mix together until combined.

5. Spray waffle iron with nonstick spray. Pour batter evenly into waffle iron and close. Cook for about 4 minutes or until golden brown.

6. Top with sliced bananas or sugar-free maple syrup and enjoy!

LUNCH

11. Buttermilk Fried Chicken

Prep: 30 min

Inactive: 1 hr

Cook: 30 min

Yield: 4 servings

Ingredients

- 1 (3 1/2 pound) chicken, cut into 8 pieces
- 2 cups buttermilk
- Salt
- Vegetable oil, for frying
- 1 cup self-rising flour
- 1/2 teaspoon sweet paprika
- Freshly ground pepper
- 1/4 teaspoon garlic powder

Directions

1. Toss the chicken, buttermilk and 1 teaspoon salt in a bowl. Cover and refrigerate, 1 hour.

2. Heat 1 inch of vegetable oil in a large deep skillet over medium-high heat until a deep-fry thermometer registers 360.

3. Mix the flour, paprika, 1/4 teaspoon pepper and the garlic powder in a shallow bowl. Remove the dark meat from the buttermilk, shake off the excess and roll in the flour mixture. Shake off the excess flour, place in the hot oil and fry, turning occasionally, until golden brown and cooked through, about 15 minutes (adjust the heat as needed). Drain on paper towels.

4. Reheat the oil to 360 degrees F. Repeat with the chicken breasts and wings, frying for about 15 minutes. Serve hot or at room temperature.

12. Garlic Mashed Potatoes

Prep time: 5 minutes

Cook time: 40 minutes

Yield: Serves 4-6

Ingredients

- 1 head of garlic
- 1 tablespoon extra virgin olive oil
- 2 pounds potatoes, preferably Yukon Gold or another yellow, waxy potato
- Salt
- 1/3 cup cream
- 3 Tbsp butter

Directions

1. Roast the garlic: Preheat the oven to 400°F. Remove the outer layer of papery skin of the whole garlic head, leaving the head itself intact.

2. Using a paring knife, slice off the tops (1/4-inch to 1/2-inch) of the garlic cloves so they are all exposed. Drizzle olive oil over the garlic heads, salt lightly, and wrap lightly in aluminum foil.

3. Bake at 400°F for 30 to 40 minutes, or until the cloves feel soft to the touch and are beginning to brown. (See

our Roasted Garlic recipe). Remove from the oven and let cool.

4. Boil the potatoes: While the garlic is roasting, peel and chop the potatoes into 1-inch chunks. Place potatoes in a medium saucepan, add 1/2 teaspoon salt, cover with cold water.

5. Bring the pot to a boil, reduce to a simmer, and simmer your potatoes until tender when pierced with a fork, about 15 minutes.

6. Warm the cream and melt the butter together, either in a small pan on the stovetop or in a bowl in the microwave.

7. Mash potatoes with garlic, cream, butter: Drain the pot with the potatoes and put it back on the stovetop over low heat. Put the drained potatoes back in the pot.

8. Squeeze the roasted garlic into the potatoes and begin mashing with a potato masher or a large fork.

9. Add the cream and butter and mash until the potatoes are the consistency you want. Do not over-beat them, or they potatoes will become gummy.

10. Taste for salt and add some if needed.

13. Stuffing Stock

Prep Time: 15 Minutes

Cook Time: 55 Minutes

Total Time: 1 Hour 10 Minutes

Servings: 12 Servings

Ingredients

- 2 small onions diced
- 4 stalks celery diced
- 2/3 cup butter
- 1 1/2 teaspoons poultry seasoning or 1/2 teaspoon ground sage
- black pepper
- salt to taste
- 12 cups bread cubes
- 3-4 cups chicken broth
- 2 tablespoons fresh parsley
- 1 tablespoon fresh herbs sage, thyme, rosemary

Instructions

1.   Preheat oven to 350F.
2. Melt butter in a large skillet over medium heat. Add onion, celery and poultry seasoning (and rosemary if

using). Cook over medium-low until tender (do not brown), about 10-12 minutes.

3. Place bread cubes in a large bowl. Add onion mixture, parsley and fresh herbs.

4. Pour broth overtop until cubes are moist (but not soggy) and gently toss. You may not need all of the broth. Season with salt and pepper to taste.

5. Place mixture in a serving dish, dot with additional butter and cover.

6. Bake 35 minutes, uncover and bake an additional 10 minutes.

14. Spinach Fish Rolls

Ingredients

- 1 pound sole, orange roughy or flounder fillets
- 1 1/2 cups firmly packed spinach leaves
- 1/4 teaspoon garlic salt
- 1/3 cup fat-free mayonnaise or salad dressing
- 1/2 teaspoon Dijon mustard
- 1/4cup garlic-flavored croutons, crushed
- wedge, if desired

Directions

1. Heat oven to 400°F. Spray square baking dish, 8x8x2 inches, with cooking spray. If fish fillets are large, cut into 4 serving pieces.
2. Place spinach on fish; sprinkle with garlic salt. Roll up each fillet, beginning at narrow end. Place rolls, with points underneath, in baking dish. Mix mayonnaise and mustard; spoon onto each roll. Sprinkle with crushed croutons.
3. Bake uncovered 15 to 20 minutes or until fish flakes easily with fork. Serve with lemon wedges.

15. Moist Roast Chicken

Ready In: 1hr 15mins

Serves: 4-6

Yield: 1 Whole Chicken

Ingredients

- 1 -3 lb roasting chicken
- 1 1/2 tablespoons olive oil
- 1 teaspoon salt
- 1 teaspoon ground black pepper
- 1/2 teaspoon dried oregano
- 1 teaspoon dried basil
- 1 teaspoon paprika

Directions

1. Preheat your oven to 450 degrees before starting to prepare the chicken.
2. Place the whole chicken into a medium sized baking pan.
3. Rub the entire bird with the olive oil.
4. In a small bowl combine the salt, pepper, oregano, basil, and paprika, then sprinkle evenly over chicken.

5. In the preheated oven bake the chicken for 20 minutes.

6. Lower the oven to 400 degrees.

7. Continue baking for 40-50 minutes, or until golden brown and juices run clear.

8. If your chicken looks like it is browning too quickly, lay a sheet of tin foil over the top loosely and it will slow down the browning for you.

9. Let the chicken rest in its juices for at least 10 minutes before carving and serving. (This lets the bird reabsorb some of the juices and helps to make it even more moist.).

16. Gaus Chicken

Serves: About 4

Ingredients

Chicken

- 1 1/2 lbs. boneless skinless chicken breast, cut into chunks
- 2 Tbls. garlic powder
- 2 Tbls. powdered ginger
- 1/4 cup flour
- canola oil, for frying

Breading

- 3 eggs
- 3/4 cup flour

Sauce

- 1/4 cup light soy sauce
- 1/3 cup Triple Sec
- 2 Tbls. sugar
- 3 Tbls. rice wine vinegar
- 2 1/2 Tbls. fresh ginger, grated

- 1 Tbls. Aleppo chili flakes
- 1 large orange, juice and zest

Garnish

- Sesame seeds
- Fresh green onion, sliced
- Chili flakes

Serve with

- Steamed white rice (we like jasmine or basmati).

Instructions

1. Prep the chicken: Toss the chicken chunks into a gallon-sized zip-top bag or a large bowl. Add the ginger and garlic powder. Seal the bag and toss to coat. Toss in the flour. Toss to coat again. Set that aside for a sec.
2. Beat the eggs in a medium-sized bowl.
3. Put 3/4 of a cup of flour on a large plate or bowl. You're ready to start breading the chicken. Set out a clean plate for the chicken once it's dipped and floured.
4. Bread the chicken: Take a piece of chicken. Drop it into the beaten egg and coat it on all sides quickly. Then drop it onto the plate of flour. Toss to coat. Put the battered chicken on your clean plate. Repeat with the rest of the chicken until it's all coated. Set the chicken

aside for a minute while you make the sauce and heat the oil.

5. Make the sauce: Put the soy sauce, Triple Sec, and sugar in a bowl. And the rice wine vinegar. Toss in the fresh grated ginger, chili flakes, and orange zest. Squeeze in the juice. Whisk it up. Give it a taste. Adjust the seasoning if you like, adding a little more soy to make it saltier, or sugar to make it sweeter. This is the basic flavor of the dish, so be sure you're happy with it. Set it aside while you fry the chicken.

6. Fry the chicken: Pour about a quarter inch of canola oil in a large, flat-bottomed pan. Set it on the stove over high heat for a few minutes, until the surface of the oil starts to shimmer. While you're waiting, set a plate next to the stove to catch the chicken when it's cooked. The oil is hot enough to fry when you dip a piece of chicken in and the oil starts to bubble rapidly immediately. When the oil is hot enough, add the chicken to the pan carefully. Fry for a few minutes on one side. When the chicken is golden brown and crunchy on the bottom, flip it all over. When the bottom is equally golden brown and crunchy, remove the chicken from the pan with a spider or large, slotted spoon. Transfer the cooked chicken to your waiting plate.

7. Sauce and toss the chicken: Pour out most the oil and add the chicken back to the pan. Turn the heat on medium-high, and pour the sauce over the chicken.

8. Stir to coat. The sauce should start to bubble up rapidly, so keep tossing it. Toss until the sauce thickens and reduces to the consistency of warm jam. It should be thick enough that you can see the bottom of the pan as you stir.

9. Serve over steamed white rice, sprinkled with sliced green onion, sesame seeds, and a pinch of chili flakes.

17. Butternut Squash Stew

Prep: 30 m

Cook: 1 h 30 m

Ready In: 2 h

Ingredients

- 3 tablespoons olive oil
- 1 large white onion, diced
- 1 tablespoon ground cinnamon
- 2 tablespoons chili powder
- 4 cloves crushed garlic
- 1 tablespoon cumin seeds, toasted
- 2 tablespoons fresh lemon juice
- 4 large tomatoes - peeled, seeded, and coarsely chopped
- 1 medium acorn squash, peeled and diced
- 1 cup pinto beans, cooked or canned
- 1 cup water
- salt and pepper to taste

Directions

1. In a large heavy-bottomed pot, heat olive oil and saute the onion for a few minutes. Add the cinnamon and chili powder and continue to saute for another 2 minutes. Mix in the garlic and cumin seeds, saute for 2 minutes more before adding lemon juice and the tomatoes. Mix thoroughly so the stew doesn't get too chunky.

2. Stir the squash, pinto beans and water into the stew. Season with salt and pepper to taste. Let the stew simmer for 1 hour, or until squash is tender. Stirring occasionally throughout the cooking hour, and add more water if necessary. The finished stew should have a nice, thick stewy texture.

3. Heat a large skillet over a medium-high heat. Place one piece of pita bread at a time into the skillet. When one side of the pita bread gets hot, flip the bread over and heat the other side; approximately 1 minute of cooking per side. Serve the stew with the heated pita bread.

18. Tuna Salad

Ingredients

All you need for this recipe are a few essential ingredients.

- Canned Tuna: 2.5 ounces
- Mayonnaise: 1/4 cup
- Celery: 1 stalk (diced)
- Red Onion: 2 tablespoon (diced)
- Parsley: 1-2 tablespoon (chopped)
- Dijon Mustard: 1/2 tablespoon
- Salt and Pepper: to taste

Directions

1. Drain the liquid from the tuna cans.
2. Add the tuna, mayonnaise, diced celery, diced red onion, herbs, Dijon mustard, salt and pepper to a mixing bowl. Stir together until well combined.

19. Spinach Salad

Total: 1 hr

Prep: 15 min

Inactive: 20 min

Cook: 25 min

Yield: 6 servings

Ingredients

- 3 whole eggs
- Ice
- 7 slices thick-cut peppered bacon
- 1 small whole red onion
- 1 package white button mushrooms
- 3 tablespoons red wine vinegar
- 2 teaspoons sugar
- 1/2 teaspoon Dijon mustard
- 1 dash salt
- 8 ounces baby spinach, washed, dried and stems removed

Directions

1. Place the eggs in a saucepan, cover with water and bring to a boil. Then turn off the heat and allow to sit in the water for 20 minutes. Drain off the water and add ice on top of the eggs.

2. Fry the bacon in a skillet until crispy/chewy. Remove to a paper towel. Drain the fat into a bowl and reserve. Give the skillet a wipe with kitchen paper.

3. Slice the red onion very thinly, and then add to the skillet. Cook slowly until the onions are caramelized and reduced. Remove to a plate and set aside.

4. Slice the mushrooms and add them to the same skillet with a little of the reserved bacon fat if needed. Cook slowly until caramelized and brown. Remove to a plate and set aside. Chop the bacon. Peel and slice the eggs.

5. Make the hot bacon dressing:

6. Add 3 tablespoons of the reserved bacon fat, vinegar, sugar, Dijon and salt to a small saucepan or skillet over medium-low heat. Whisk together and heat thoroughly until bubbly. Add the spinach to a large bowl. Arrange the onions, mushrooms and bacon on top. Pour the hot dressing over the top; toss to combine. Arrange the eggs over the top and serve.

7. Per serving: Calories 270; Total Fat 22.5 grams; Saturated Fat 7.5 grams; Protein 10 grams; Total Carbohydrate 7 grams; Sugar: 2 grams; Fiber 2 grams; Cholesterol 123 milligrams; Sodium 526 milligrams.

20. Notato Salad

Prep Time: 30 mins

Cook Time: 10 mins

Total Time: 40 mins

Servings: 8

Ingredients

- 2 Eggs

- 6 tablespoons Egg White

- 1 head Cauliflower 1 kg / 2.2 pounds unpeeled

- 2 stalks Celery chopped (including leaves)

- 3 Green Onions chopped (including stalks)

- 1 Bell Pepper chopped (any colour)

- 4 Radishes sliced, thin

- 2 tablespoons Instant Mashed Potato Flakes

- 1/2 teaspoon Onion Powder

- 1/2 teaspoon Garlic Powder

- 1 teaspoon Salt

- 1 teaspoon Ground Pepper

- 1 teaspoon Sugar

- 1/2 teaspoon Celery Seed

- 1 tablespoon Lemon Juice

- 1 tablespoon Mustard prepared

- 2 tablespoons Sweet Pickle Relish

- 6 tablespoons Mayonnaise low-fat

Instructions

1. Lightly-spray an oven-proof bowl, jug or dish with cooking spray. Crack the 2 eggs into it; add the egg white. Microwave on high until yolks and white are set, about 1:40 minutes to 2 minutes depending on your microwave. Then remove and set aside to cool while you push on with the rest of the recipe.

2. Remove leaves and stalk from cauliflower, chop into quite small florets, and wash. Put in a covered container with a bit of water and microwave *just* until a fork goes in easily; no longer [See cooking

notes / tips below.] Drain, and plunge into cold water bath to cool.

3. Assemble all the other ingredients down to the celery seed in a large bowl. Chop the egg and add; toss. Add the final 4 wet ingredients (the juice, mustard, relish and mayo), stir, then add the well-drained cauliflower (ideally, if you can, spin the cauliflower in a salad spinner just before adding to salad mixture to get rid of any water trapped in the "curd" of the cauliflower.) Fold gently -- a pair of clean hands work best. Put in covered container in fridge and chill for at least 3 hours before serving.

4. You can make this a day or two ahead safely if you are using commercially bottled mayonnaise and store the salad covered in the refrigerator.

5. Optional: serve from a bowl garnished with fresh-chopped parsley and a few sprinkles of paprika.

DINNER

21. Banana Bread

Prep time: 10 minutes

Cook time: 55 minutes

Yield: Makes one loaf

Ingredients

- 2 to 3 very ripe bananas, peeled (about 1 1/4 to 1 1/2 cups mashed)
- 1/3 cup melted butter, unsalted or salted
- 1 teaspoon baking soda
- Pinch of salt
- 3/4 cup sugar (1/2 cup if you would like it less sweet, 1 cup if more sweet)
- 1 large egg, beaten
- 1 teaspoon vanilla extract
- 1 1/2 cups of all-purpose flour

Directions

1. Preheat the oven to 350°F (175°C), and butter a 4x8-inch loaf pan.

2. In a mixing bowl, mash the ripe bananas with a fork until completely smooth. Stir the melted butter into the mashed bananas.

3. Mix in the baking soda and salt. Stir in the sugar, beaten egg, and vanilla extract. Mix in the flour.

4. Pour the batter into your prepared loaf pan. Bake for 50 minutes to 1 hour at 350°F (175°C), or until a tester inserted into the center comes out clean.

5. Remove from oven and let cool in the pan for a few minutes. Then remove the banana bread from the pan and let cool completely before serving. Slice and serve. (A bread knife helps to make slices that aren't crumbly.)

22. Hard Boiled Eggs

Prep Time: 5 Mins

Total Time: 20 Mins

Yields: 12

Ingredients

- 12 large eggs
- water

Directions

1. Place eggs in a large pot and cover by an inch of cold water. Place pot on stove and bring to a boil. Instantly turn off heat and cover pot. Let sit for 11 minutes.

2. Remove from pan and transfer ice water. Let cool 2 minutes before peeling and serving.

23. Roasted Vegetable Puree

Prep Time: 10 Min

Cook Time: 40 Min

Total Time: 50 Min

Serve: 5

Ingredients

- Fresh vegetables
- 2 teaspoons oil
- Breast milk or formula
- Some suggestions for vegetables to roast include:
- Potato
- Kumara
- Yam
- Carrot
- Parsnip
- Pumpkin

Directions

1. Preheat the oven to 180 degrees Celsius.
2. Peel and slice vegetables.
3. Drizzle with oil.

4. Place in an oven tray and bake for 30 to 40 minutes until soft.

5. Remove from the oven and leave to cool for five minutes.

6. Mash with a potato masher. Or purée in a food processor or blender until smooth.

7. Stir through enough breast milk or formula to make a smooth purée.

8. Freeze leftover cooled purée in ice cube trays.

24. Butternut Squash Rossoto

Prep Time: 15 Mins

Total Time: 55 Mins

Yields: 8 Servings

Ingredients

- 7 c. low-sodium chicken broth
- 1 tbsp. extra-virgin olive oil
- 1 small onion, chopped
- 2 tbsp. butter, divided
- 4 c. cubed butternut squash (from a 2 1/2-lb. squash)
- 3 cloves garlic, minced
- 2 c. arborio rice
- 1/2 c. white wine
- 1 c. freshly grated Parmesan
- 2 tbsp. freshly chopped sage

Directions

1. In a medium saucepan over medium heat, bring chicken broth to a simmer. Reduce heat to low.
2. In a large pot or Dutch oven, heat oil. Add onion and cook, stirring often, until beginning to soften, about 5 minutes. Stir in squash, 1 tablespoon butter and garlic. Cook until

the squash is beginning to color around edges and then soft, about 6 minutes. Season with salt and pepper.

3. Stir in remaining tablespoon butter arborio rice, stirring quickly. Cook until the grains are well-coated and smell slightly toasty, about 2 minutes. Add the wine and cook until the wine has mostly absorbed.

4. With a ladle, add about 1 cup hot broth. Stirring often, cook until the rice has mostly absorbed liquid. Add remaining broth about 1 cup at a time, continuing to allow the rice to absorb each addition of broth before adding more.

5. Stir often and cook until squash is tender and risotto is al dente and creamy, not mushy, about 25 minutes. Stir in Parmesan and sage, then season with salt and pepper before serving.

25. Whipped Sweet Potatoes

Total: 55 min

Prep: 10 min

Cook: 45 min

Yield: 10 to 12 servings

Ingredients

- 4 large sweet potatoes, scrubbed
- Kosher salt and freshly ground black pepper
- 2 cups heavy cream
- 2 bay leaves
- 1/2 teaspoon ground cinnamon
- Pinch freshly grated nutmeg
- 1/2 orange, zested
- 2 tablespoons brown sugar
- 1 tablespoon unsalted butter

Directions

1. Preheat the oven to 350 degrees F.
2. Prick the sweet potatoes all over with a fork, drizzle with olive oil and season with salt and pepper. Put them in a roasting pan and roast for 45 minutes until they are very soft. Remove the pan from the oven.

3. In a small sauce pot, over low heat, heat the cream with the bay leaves, then keep warm until ready to puree potatoes. Discard the bay leaves before adding to potatoes.

4. When the potatoes are cool enough to handle, scoop the flesh into the bowl of a food processor. Season with salt, cinnamon, nutmeg, orange zest, and brown sugar. Add cream and 1 tablespoon of butter and puree until super smooth.

26. Sweet Potato Soup

Preparation Time: Less Than 30 Mins

Cooking Time: 10 To 30 Mins

Serves: Serves 3–4

Ingredients

- 1 tbsp olive oil
- 1 onion, roughly chopped
- 2 large carrots, peeled and roughly chopped
- 4cm/1½ inches fresh root ginger, finely chopped
- 1 garlic clove, crushed
- ½ tsp dried red chilli flakes
- 700g/1lb 10oz sweet potatoes, peeled and cubed
- 1.2 litres/2 pints vegetable stock
- salt and freshly ground black pepper

Directions

1. Heat the oil in a large, lidded saucepan over a medium-high heat. Add the onion and carrots and cook until softened. Stir in the ginger, garlic and chilli flakes and fry for 2–3 minutes, or until fragrant.

2. Stir in the sweet potatoes and stock. Turn up the heat and bring the pan to the boil. Reduce the heat to low and simmer with the lid on for 15 minutes, or until the sweet potato is tender.

3. Remove the pan from the heat and blend the soup, using a stick blender, until smooth. Alternatively, tip it into a food processor and blend. Season to taste and serve.

27. Blueberry Soup

Prep Time: 5 Min

Cooking Time: 15 Min

Total Time: 20 Min

Serve: 2 to 3

Ingredients

- 3 cups blueberries, fresh or frozen
- 2 tablespoons honey
- 2 teaspoons lemon juice
- 1 cinnamon stick, optional
- 2 teaspoons cornstarch
- 1 teaspoon lemon zest
- Yogurt for serving, if desired

Directions

1. Combine the berries with the honey, lemon juice, cinnamon stick if using (it's traditional, but I generally don't use any) and a cup of water. Bring to a gentle boil, then turn down to a low simmer, cover and cook 8-10 minutes, until the berries are stewed. (At this point, it's also traditional to strain the berry skins out and just

use the juice, but I like to leave them in for more texture.)

2. Stir the cornstarch into 1 Tbs. of warm water to make a slurry, then stir this into the cooked berries. Bring back to a very gentle boil and cook, stirring, until starting to thicken, about 2 minutes. Remove from the heat and stir in the lemon zest.

3. Serve warm, or chill and serve later. Top with a scoop of yogurt before serving (or use whipped cream or creme fraiche instead of yogurt if you'd like to make this a dessert).

28. Carrot Soup

Total: 50 mins

Servings: 8

Ingredients

- 1 tablespoon butter
- 1 tablespoon extra-virgin olive oil
- 1 medium onion, chopped
- 1 stalk celery, chopped
- 2 cloves garlic, chopped
- 1 teaspoon chopped fresh thyme or parsley
- 5 cups chopped carrots
- 2 cups water
- 4 cups reduced-sodium chicken broth, "no-chicken" broth (see Note) or vegetable broth
- ½ cup half-and-half (optional)
- ½ teaspoon salt
- Freshly ground pepper to taste

Directions

1. Heat butter and oil in a Dutch oven over medium heat until the butter melts. Add onion and celery; cook, stirring occasionally, until softened, 4 to 6 minutes.

Add garlic and thyme (or parsley); cook, stirring, until fragrant, about 10 seconds.

2. Stir in carrots. Add water and broth; bring to a lively simmer over high heat. Reduce heat to maintain a lively simmer and cook until very tender, about 25 minutes.

3. Puree the soup in batches in a blender until smooth. (Use caution when pureeing hot liquids.) Stir in half-and-half (if using), salt and pepper.

29. Onion and Apple Soup

Prep Time: 1 Hour 10 Mins

Total Time: 2 Hours

Yield: Makes 8 cups

Direction

1. Melt butter in a large Dutch oven over low heat.
   Add onions and next 2 ingredients, and cook,
   stirring often, 30 to 35 minutes or until onions are
   caramel colored. (Adjust heat to prevent
   scorching.) Add apples, and cook, stirring often, 5
   minutes. Add broth and next 2 ingredients.
   Increase heat to medium, and bring to a boil,
   stirring occasionally. Reduce heat to medium-low,
   and simmer, stirring occasionally, 20 to 25 minutes
   or until apples and potato are tender. Remove from
   heat, and let stand 15 minutes. Discard bay leaf.

2. Process mixture with a handheld blender until
   smooth. Add cream and lemon juice. Return to low
   heat; simmer, stirring often, 15 minutes. Add salt
   and pepper. Serve with Cheese Puff Pastries.

30. Lima Bean Soup

Prep: 10 Min

Cook: 30 Min

Total Time: 40 Min

Makes: 12 servings (3 quarts)

Ingredients

- 3 cans (14-1/2 ounces each) chicken broth
- 2 cans (15-1/4 ounces each) lima beans, rinsed and drained
- 3 medium carrots, thinly sliced
- 2 medium potatoes, peeled and diced
- 2 small sweet red peppers, chopped
- 2 small onions, chopped
- 2 celery ribs, thinly sliced
- 1/4 cup butter
- 1-1/2 teaspoons dried marjoram
- 1/2 teaspoon salt
- 1/2 teaspoon pepper
- 1/2 teaspoon dried oregano
- 1 cup half-and-half cream
- 3 bacon strips, cooked and crumbled

Directions

1. In a Dutch oven or soup kettle, combine the first 12 ingredients; bring to a boil over medium heat. Reduce heat; cover and simmer for 25-35 minutes or until vegetables are tender.
2. Add cream; heat through but do not boil. Sprinkle with bacon just before serving.

www.ingramcontent.com/pod-product-compliance
Lightning Source LLC
Chambersburg PA
CBHW050915170626
46733CB00072B/974